A Day at School

A Hello Reader! Activity Book

ISBN 0-590-69255-0

Written by Gina Shaw
Illustrated by Joan Holub

SCHOLASTIC INC.

New York Toronto London Auckland Sydney

Pam and Ben Bear are on their way to school! Look at the pictures and decide the correct order of the story. Write 1, 2, 3, or 4 in the box next to each picture. Then read the sentences and write 1, 2, 3, or 4 next to each one.

Pam and Ben walk to the bus stop._____

Pam and Ben ride the bus._____

Pam and Ben say good-bye to Meg._____

Pam and Ben get on the bus._____

In the School Yard

Before the school bell rings, Pam and Ben play in the yard with their friends. Read the sentences below and follow the directions.

1. Color the small ball pink.
2. Color one teacher's dress red.
3. Color two trees green.
4. Color one flower yellow.
5. Color two pairs of sneakers black.

Pam and Ben are in different classrooms. Draw a line along each one's path. When you find Pam's classroom, write **Pam** on the door. Write **Ben** on the door of Ben's classroom.

Ben   Pam

Room 101   Room 102   Room 103

·········· Caring for the Class Pets ··········

The children in Ben's class take care of their pets. Look at the picture, then read the sentences. Draw a circle around **YES** or **NO** to answer each sentence.

1. There are four pets.   YES   NO

2. A boy is tearing paper.   YES   NO

3. There is a goldfish in the tank.   YES   NO

4. A girl is feeding the hamster.   YES   NO

5. A girl is putting a big shell
   in the crab's tank.   YES   NO

·········· Let's Hear It for Books! ··········

The children in Pam's class draw pictures of their favorite books. Ms. Honey Bear puts the drawings around the room. In the empty box, draw a picture of your favorite book. Be sure to include the name of the book.

Clifford, the Big Red Dog

Look at the patterns. For each one, circle the shape that comes next.

1. ■ ◆ ■ ◆ ■ ◆ ■ ◆ ■ ◆ ■ ◆

a. ■　　　　b. ◆　　　　c. ■ ■　　　　d. ◆ ◆

2. ★ • ★ ★ •• ★ • ★ ★ •• ★ •

a. ★　　　　b. •　　　　c. ★ ★　　　　d. ••

3. ○●○　●○●　○●○　●○●

a. ○○●　　b. ●○○●　　c. ○●○　　d. ●●○

4. ⌒ ⌣ ⌒⌒ ⌣⌣ ⌒⌒⌒ ⌣⌣⌣ ⌒⌒⌒⌒

a. ⌒⌣　　b. ⌣⌣⌣⌣　　c. ⌒⌒⌒　　d. ⌣⌣⌒

Animals All Around Us

In science, Pam's class is studying about animals. Ms. Honey Bear is asking questions. Help Pam answer each question below. Circle each correct answer.

1.. Which one can fly?

2. Which one hops?

3. Which one lives in a pond?

4. Which one has fur?

5. Which one runs fast?

6. Which one carries its baby?

Lunchtime!

Pam and Ben are in the lunchroom. First, they will eat their lunch. Then they will play outside. Look at the picture. Find all the foods hidden in the scene. Find all the playthings that are hidden. Color them.

How many different foods did you find?_____

How many different playthings did you find?_____

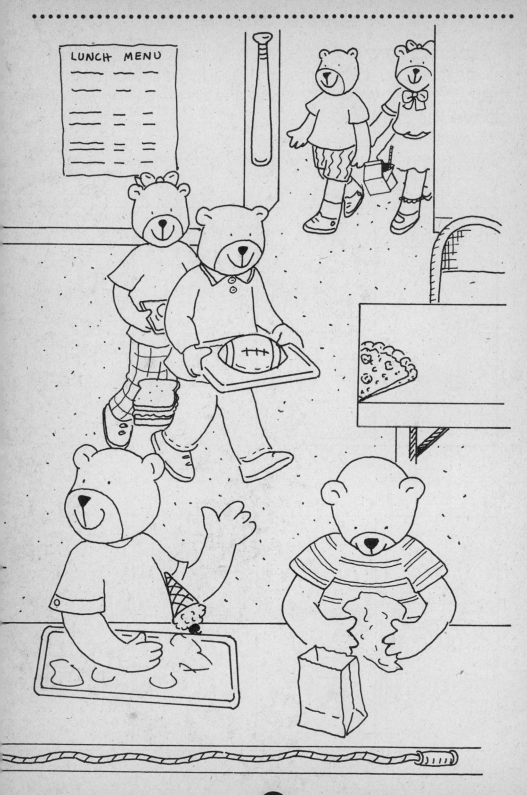

Let's Share!

It's sharing time in Pam's class. Some children have things to share. Look at each group of pictures. Put them in order. Write 1, 2, 3, or 4 in the small boxes above the pictures.

What would you bring to sharing time?

Draw a picture and write a sentence about it here.

The Art Class

The children in Ben's class are painting pictures. Help them finish their paintings. Read the words under each picture and add a drawing of the word shown. Color your drawing.

a red apple

a blue pail

a yellow sun

a green hat

purple balloons

a white and pink cake

·······Who Works at School?·······

Find all of the people who work at school. Follow the directions.

1. Put a triangle on the library teacher.

2. Put a rectangle on the person who works in the lunchroom.

3. Put an **X** on the worker who helps children across the street.

4. Put an oval on the principal.

5. Put a ✔ on the teacher working at the computer.

6. Put a circle on the worker who is cleaning a classroom.

7. Color the picture of the students and teacher.

Ms. Honey Bear asks Pam to take a note to the office. But Pam doesn't know how to get to the office. Help Pam. Read the sentences on the next page. Look at the pictures. Draw a line for each direction Pam takes.

1. Go from Pam to the gym.

2. Now go from the gym to the computer room.

3. Go from the computer room to the stage.

   Oops! This is not right.

4. Go to the office. The teacher is waving to you.

The End of the Day

It is time to go home. The teacher gives the class instructions. Read the sentences below. Choose the correct word to complete each sentence. Write the words in the puzzle.

1. Get your_____.

boats   books

2. Put away your_____.

pencils   sunglasses

3. Clear off your_____.

desks   shirts

4. Put on your_____.

coats   gloves

5. _____up.

Sit   Line

6. Say _____to your friends.

hello   good-bye

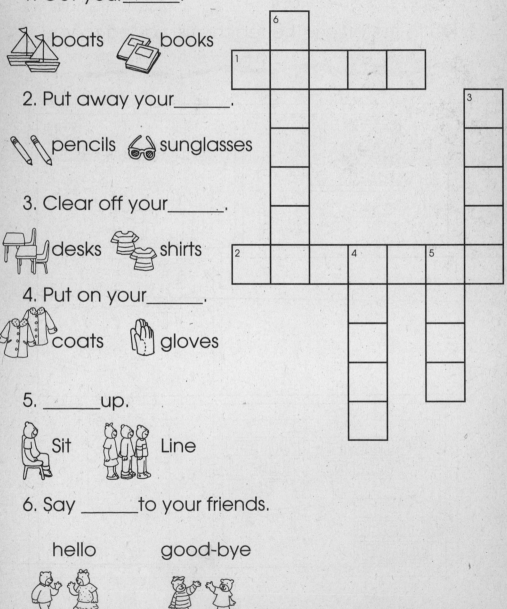

We're Home!

Pam and Ben are happy to see Meg.

1. Place a check in the box next to the things that either Pam or Ben did at school.

☐ took care of the class pets   ☐ ate lunch   ☐ went swimming

☐ answered questions   ☐ danced   ☐ drew pictures

"I am so glad you're home now," said Meg. "I missed you both so much!"

2. What do you think Meg said next? Underline the right sentence.

"Good morning! It's time for school!"

"Will you play a game with me?"

"Now, it's my turn to go to the store."

So Pam, Ben, and Meg played "school" together all afternoon!

Page 2

Pam and Ben walk to the bus stop.   2

Pam and Ben ride the bus.   4

Pam and Ben say good-bye to Meg.   1

Pam and Ben get on the bus.   3

Page 3

Readers' answers may vary.

Page 4

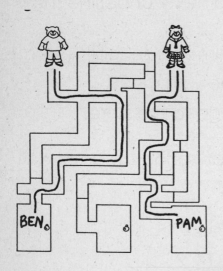

Page 5

1. YES
2. YES
3. NO
4. NO
5. YES

Pages 6-7:

Readers' answers may vary.

Page 8

1. b
2. c
3. c
4. b

Page 9

1.   4

2.   5.

3.   6.

Pages 10-11

How many different foods did you find?   6

How many different toys did you find?   5

Pages 12-13

1.	2	3	1	4
2.	4	1	3	2
3.	3	1	2	4

Pages 14-15

Page 20

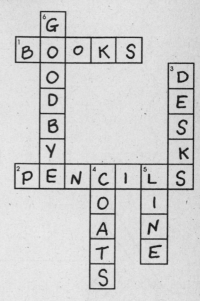

Pages 16-17

Pages 18-19

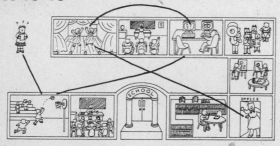

Page 21:

1. ☑ took care of the class pets ☑ ate lunch ☐ went swimming

   ☑ answered questions ☐ danced ☑ drew pictures

2. "Will you play a game with me?"

Thank you,

_____

(your name)

for coming to school with us!
Your friends,
Pam and Ben Bear

752. Nick